ATYPICAL CELLS OF UNDETERMINED SIGNIFICANCE

Essays & Poems

Brenna Womer

C&R Press
Conscious & Responsible

Summer Tide Pool Chapbook
2017 Fourth Collection Selection 1 of 1 CB8

Printed in the United States of America

First Edition
1 2 3 4 5 6 7 8 9

Cover Design by Max Rippon
Interior Design by Laura Metter

ISBN: 978-1-936196-62-3

C&R Press
Conscious & Responsible
www.crpress.org

For special discounted bulk purchases please contact:
C&R Press sales@crpress.org

ATYPICAL CELLS OF UNDETERMINED SIGNIFICANCE

]

CONTENTS

Male Doctors & My Anatomy

I.

His fingers are freckled and hairy and sausage-thick, and he waits until he's palpating my ovaries to ask how classes are going.

You're almost done now, hey?

He's been asking this question since I was a senior in high school. Now in the second year of my Master's, I just say

Yep

because I don't like the way my body tightens around his fingers when I speak.

Your grandparents came into town for a checkup just last week, he says.

He tells me to untie the front of my gown and raise my arms.

Try to touch the ceiling, he says.

He breathes, hot and wet, into cupped hands before fingering my breasts the way a child bangs their way up and down a piano in feigned familiarity.

They're good people, he says, but I've forgotten who he's talking about.

II.

He's wearing blue jeans.

Does it smell like a can of tunafish? he asks, and I hate that he says "tuna fish" like it's one word.

I see my mother draining albacore in water over the sink for casserole night, pressing the metal lid into dry, flaky meat. Juice squirts and drips.

No, I say. (I lie.)

His phone buzzes in its holster, and he holds up a finger; he takes the call. He presses a few buttons and then hangs up.

It was a survey, he says.

He diagnoses me without lifting up my gown, because, at this point, we both hate my tunafish cunt.

III.

He draws a house and a stoop and a path to the front gate, to the curbside mailbox.

He draws a stick figure one step down from the door.

This is you, he says, pointing to the stick.

The house is healthy, and the mailbox is cervical cancer. I'm trying to keep you from checking the mail.

He hands me the drawing.
>*For your fridge*, he says.

IV.

He tells me to
>*Lean back, feet in the stirrups. Scoot-your-boot down to the edge of the table.*

He tells me to
>*Relax.*

The scope is large and white and attached to an arm like an optometry phoropter, but this doctor is looking for precancerous cells so much smaller than letters at the bottom of an eye chart.
>*I'll be swabbing your cervix with a hand-mop soaked in vinegar,* he says.
>*Think of it like I'm making a salad in your vagina.*

When he's finished, he shakes my hand and leaves me with a pamphlet that warns of post-procedure stench and spotting and cramps. That tells me not to be alarmed by the deposit of a thick, black scab in a day or two. I put my underwear back on; I wash my hands.

When a Psychic Says We're Soul Mates

You expect room,
space
beyond pines;
Kings of Up, Sideways.
For a good time, die, forever.
Bible tells me bodies hurt,
perfect beasts—wild, dark,
promised.

Years of silver, play china.
This is the runaway; the last,
smashed, alone I love you.
This waltz in the woods (the
stone, the show, dumb sky,
paranormal sunshine). A little
galaxy, misery; hills spark
green. Few men take this walk,
this war. Night rises and the
whale, dog, spider, frail cock:
things I hate.

Spy our keepers; the last days,
nights. Rise, Brother! Magic
child, seeking. End the days
now, white heart (magnolia—)
my best shame.
You horrible paradise:
lost, lost, lost.

We talk about love, the retreat,
and who lives, hearts blue, and
cigarettes, and the girl in the
realms of dilemma, running
clueless with grizzly hours,
getting fat.

Recall how you know the heart,
and remember the future, the
brain, the chronic hunger and
burn; life in a wet summer, loud
and close—eternal, intolerable.

Number the young.

Empire Blue

Fort Monroe, Virginia, 2003

We drove in the day before Hurricane Isabel with our lives blocking the rear view of our Ford Expedition. There was no available housing on Langley Air Force Base, so we were assigned to a duplex on Fort Monroe, a neighboring Army base. Fort Monroe is an island in the Chesapeake Bay connected by a short bridge to the Virginia mainland. Our little home was two stories of crumbling red brick, and after the hurricane washed saltwater over the island, everything green turned brown or gray. We would turn back and drive inland to ride out the storm, but not before standing on the seawall together, Mom, Dad, and I, to watch a fleet of Naval ships and submarines from Norfolk set out toward the horizon, for safety.

My mother grew up the middle child of a poor Navy family, and from the time she was born, she moved every two years. She was shy and fearful, the worst-case-scenario for a perpetual new girl. She said she wore dresses too short, even by 1970s standards, because new ones cost money her parents didn't have. Her father was a harsh man—a submariner, a pipe smoker, and a hothead. He was absent throughout her childhood, far more than my father from my own, which left her working mother greatly burdened with three children and a house to keep. Growing up, I wondered at my grandmother's grim mouth and vacant eyes in old photographs because the woman I knew was quick to laugh, full of warmth and kindness. I would learn her sepia-toned gaze was one of an eighth-grade dropout who married a sailor at fifteen to get away from an abusive, alcoholic father. It was the face of a woman who married a man with a short fuse, a man out to sea nine months of every year, a man who kept her pregnant through her late teens and early twenties. Precious years of independence, of self-discovery, lost to swollen ankles and crying babies and dinner on the table every night at five-thirty.

If you asked me what I wanted to be, from the time I was a little girl until my freshman year of college, I would have told you I wanted to be a homemaker. Grandma worked various jobs to help support a struggling household, and when I was growing up my mother worked periodically to help with credit card payments or to stave off a restlessness that still plagues her to this day. But ultimately, their lives were their children; they were homemakers. My mother's side of the family is devoutly religious—Baptist mostly—and they subscribe to Old Testament views on where a woman's value lies—in the home she keeps and the food she makes, in her children, which are her crowning glory, and in the respect she has for her husband who is the head of the household. As I transitioned into my sophomore year of college, I chose to abandon the Christian faith in which I had been raised and did my best to toss off the Southern Baptist ideologies so deeply engrained in my being. With that abandonment came many changes, including a newfound understanding of myself as a singular person, an individual without a preordained path laid out for her. For the first time my life was mine and not something I was living to honor someone else with, and while that was exhilarating, it also instigated a passionate revolt against the life my mother and grandmother had settled into. I was—am—terrified of being owned. By a god or a man or a child or a place. By anyone or anything but myself.

RAF Lakenheath, England, 1999

It was the summer of butterflies. Monarchs and painted ladies, I would later learn, but to us they were the common and uncommon butterflies, respectively. I was seven, and my friends and I spent hours catching them in whatever containers our moms let us take from the kitchen cabinets. Mine was an empty Ragu jar, the label scrubbed clean off for a full view, with holes Mom tapped into the metal lid using a Phillip's head and a hammer from Dad's olive drab, military-issue tool bag. It was my family's last summer on RAF Lakenheath, an Air Force base 80 miles north of London, and the butterfly bush in our front yard smelled sweet and delicate, like the trellis of honeysuckle over my grandparents' porch in San Diego, like the sprig of jasmine a boyfriend's Sri Lankan mother would one day tuck behind my ear.

The *Buddleja davidii,* or Empire Blue, is a cultivar heavy with cone-shaped clusters of tiny purple flowers interspersed between narrow, soft green leaves. Some know the bush as we did, a butterfly bush. They attract hummingbirds and bees as well, but we only ever saw butterflies. The bushes grow to be about five feet tall and wide, but I remember getting lost inside of it, thick as a cornfield, stalks towering above our heads so high we couldn't see our houses, so dense with purple and green we had to call out to each other, *Any luck?* The *Buddleja davidii* takes so easily to most soils that in Australia and parts of the U.S. it's considered a weed—a fragrant, seductive trespasser. It's known to thrive in areas of disruption. You can find it in a roadside ditch next to fast food cups and candy wrappers, among the rocks on a craggy mountain path, pushing through the tired cracks of a land made barren by fire; your hook might catch in its leaves as you reel in a line from the riverbank. If cut down to a stump at the end of its flowering season, it will come back fuller the following year.

In the shadows of the living room, what was left of the evening light deigning through our sliding glass doors, I asked where my mother was. It was not usual for Dad to pick me up from wherever I had been. He did not like the question, more probably did not like the answer, was not used to telling me the hard things.

"Your mother is in the hospital. She'll be there for a couple weeks."

Why?

"She's just a little sad right now."

Why?

"That's what she's trying to figure out, sweetheart."

We learned it was best to approach butterflies from behind, where we figured we were out of their line of vision, and to make a V with the lid and rim of the container. Once we were close enough to the creature slowly lowering its wings and folding them up together again, showing in turn its beauty and banality, we clapped the lid tight to the container, trapping the butterfly inside. We watched them panic, observed the colors and shapes on their wings until they calmed down and stood at the base of the container with their wings closed in silent protest against our curious stares; how warped and fish-eyed we must have looked through the curvature of the glass. When they were still and showed to us only the muddled underside of their wings, we released them back into the bush for another one of us to catch.

I remember only one visit while she was in the hospital; she took me to the art therapy room and showed me a ceramic trivet she made. She pulled it out of a little cubbyhole and we sat in plastic chairs with metal, hairpin legs—the same we had at Lakenheath Elementary. It was a mosaic of Persian blue and crimson tiles pressed into white grout, and I told her it was beautiful. I remember her in a white hospital gown peppered with pale blue dots, but she was probably wearing jeans and a T-shirt. When she came home it was all the same to me; everything was as it should be. I didn't know the reason she was sad was because she couldn't bring herself to leave my father, and I didn't know the reason she couldn't leave him was because I loved him too much, loved him enough for the both of us. *You were the glue.* The trivet has been on the kitchen counter in every home we've lived in since. It's on their counter now, stained with sauce from jars of Ragu and chipped because I'm clumsy like my mother. Yes, I am my mother's daughter.

***

Six months we lived on the little island of Fort Monroe. My parents' bedroom window looked out onto the bay and the sound of rushing water was constant; it was the silence. I was seven and had taken to collecting sea glass along the shore. By the end of our time there we had drawers full of glass—browns and greens mostly, a handful of blues and pinks. When winter came, I didn't know snow would blanket the sand and ride the waves like rodeo cowboys. I bundled up and looked for frosted chips of glass in the cold, clumped sand. I stuffed them into my pockets, their edges smooth, their surfaces almost fuzzy. They had been opaqued by decades of movement along the ocean floor. Glass beautified in its travels, refined into something desired, less common; a token of a place, of a memory.

I've always known my mother as a rebel, sensed in her a relentless urge to buck tradition, to tell whomever it was holding her to some preordained standard that they could go fuck themselves. She dropped out of high school and married her first husband at eighteen just to get out of the house. Not for the same reason her own mother had—her family was broken in different ways. My mother's first husband was a quiet man, a mechanic. She hasn't told me much about him, or perhaps there just isn't much to tell, simple as he seemed to be. He was an extra in the movie *Hamburger Hill,* and somewhere Mom still has a picture of him with Tom Cruise on the set of *Born on the Fourth of July.* After a year of marriage she enlisted in the Air Force, and a few years after that they got a divorce. She says when they were married she was restless and immature. She says she broke his heart. With this I understand I am her daughter and I think of the e.e. cummings tattoo on my right arm. I think maybe "[i carry your heart with me(i carry it in my]" was not at all about a lover but about a mother. That maybe it's her heart I carry and the deepest secret nobody knows, not even me, is that whatever I do is her doing. Maybe she was the small voice in the dark whispering, *There's more than this. Don't get com-*

fortable, and the loves I ran away from, the men I broke and the homes I left half-empty, were because her heart is there next to mine in syncopated rhythm asking me to be better, to do it right this time.

Mom was stationed in the Philippines when she took up scuba diving in Puerto Galera. When I was a teenager and charm bracelets were in vogue, she gave me a silver charm from her keepsake box. It was a dingy scuba diver in full gear, flippers and arms poised as though propelling itself through the ocean. She told me to take care of it because it was precious, but she wanted me to have it. I lost it after a couple months and even when I noticed it was gone I didn't give it much thought. I didn't realize it was a relic of the small window between my mother's first husband and my father, the only time she's ever really had to herself. I'm not saying my mother was happy during that time; I'm saying I think she was free. She gave me a token of her independence, a charm to protect like a Catholic saint, to protect me from myself. But I didn't know I would need it. How badly I would one day need to be reminded that I was my own, that I was enough. That I didn't need anyone to tell me I existed for it to be true. Mom never asked about the charm or looked for it on my bracelet, though she usually keeps a close eye on things she or the family gives to me, things of sentimental value. It was like she passed a torch and then hurried to forget the flame, now my burden to bear.

Altus AFB, Oklahoma, 2001

There were no *Buddleja davidii* on Altus Air Force Base, and not many butterflies either as I recall; maybe they despised the Oklahoma heat as much as my mother did. A shallow creek was the dividing line between enlisted and officer housing, the flowers and the trees; we lived on Honeysuckle Avenue. The Altus outside of the base gates was one of Friday night lights and Bulldog pride, smoky restaurants and beauty parlors, white T-shirts and coveralls. We went to church at First Baptist and out for lunch at Subway after, to Hastings for books and movie rentals, and to Twilight Music for my weekly guitar lesson with Mr. Eddy. In the dry heat from the sun we shared with Texas, I practiced John Denver's "Country Roads" and Patty Loveless's "Chains" in our one-car garage until little calluses formed behind the nails on my left hand. Altus was where Dad bought our purple, hail-dented Kia Sephia with the CD player he fed *Juke Box Jive* on our weekend drives for snow cones—the stand run by high school girls with long, blond ponytails who looked so different from me at age nine, with my brown everything and belly like the Laughing Buddha, they made me ache long before I finished my tropical ice.

13

I suspected I wasn't beautiful. Beauty seemed to eat less, take longer to lose its breath, and wear something other than a one-piece to the pool. At the time I thought I wasn't allowed to wear a bikini because they were immodest. We were Southern Baptist, and bikinis rivaled the scandal of VHS tapes rated PG and above, the ones my parents would feel convicted about and, as a consolation, let me smash to pieces in the driveway with a hammer. For my eighth birthday, I got a pink bikini in the mail from my grandparents, and because it was a present I knew I could talk my mother into letting me wear it. When I asked her, she was hesitant as I had anticipated, but she didn't say anything about modesty. Instead, she winced, and said without saying, *You're going to have to learn this the hard way.*

When I got to the base pool the next day I felt beauty radiating from under my cover-up. The bikini. I was there with my father who had set himself up to tan on a plastic folding chair. My mother never came with us, not that I can remember, and I suspect it was because she didn't want her body contrast next to his. Dad's only hobby was exercising. He was lean with defined abs and biceps, and he effortlessly executed the somersault-dive combo off the diving board—the envy of every showboat teenage boy in the place. How easily he caught their attention. Dad would binge on bags of mini Twix and Three Musketeers after dinner each night in front of the television and then run it off the next day. My mother bounced between diets, sneaking fun-size candies from his bags; I can't remember a time when she didn't hate her body. She resented him for how easy he made it look, for all the dinners she made him that she wasn't allowed to eat, for the way he sculpted his body while she was sharpening her mind and that it didn't matter how many books she read or Styrofoam containers she delivered for Meals On Wheels or how good of mother she was to me, she'd still catch him checking out the tall blond a few lanes down during their bowling league on Tuesday nights—*You see that woman over there? She's exactly your father's type.*

It was a rule to rinse off before getting in the pool, and so I emerged from the ladies' locker room in my new suit with my hair slicked back, Lycra clinging to my chest. My chest, which was not filling out quite as amply as the dark hairs poking out from my bikini bottoms. I sucked in my stomach, creating an unnatural cave beneath my ribcage. I placed a hand at my waist and tried not to accentuate my wide, Latina hips—destined to be referred to as "childbearing." I walked past a table of middle school boys, scrawny and pale with backward caps, drinking cans of Surge from the soda machine. I walked slowly and made eye contact with a boy at the center of the group, the skin at my thighs like Jell-o pudding with each step. He scrunched his nose, and a look of distaste mutated into a wry smile before my plain brown eyes. He turned and laughed with the boy next to him. I looked down at my stomach, which was impeding the view of my thighs, and felt shame hotter than the concrete I scuttled across to the chair where my father was tanning. I covered myself with a towel.

Instead of butterflies, in Altus we caught crawdads, little ones that swam the creek between the flowers and the trees. Our moms netted wire coat hangers with old lace for catching, and when we met at the water it didn't matter whether our dads wore stripes or bars or stars, or who saluted first. The crawdads were harder to catch; they didn't share the air with us and camouflaged against the slimy rocks, disappeared into the moss and mud. I never liked to touch the things I caught. I wanted to look at them, creatures so different from our dogs and gerbils, from myself, yet still alive and breathing. The satisfaction was in the catching, in seeing the crawdad's armor contrast against pale yellow, pincers snagging at the lace. It was cruel to keep them in tanks the way some of my friends did, the butterflies in jars; maybe not if it was all they'd ever known. But to have an endless world replaced by walls and ceilings and stale, sour air was—still is—to me a tragedy of the highest order.

***

When my parents met, they were drunk at the Enlisted Club on Osan Air Base in South Korea. Two months later, they were married and honeymooning in Seoul. Dad was still wounded from a broken engagement to a woman back home in England where he grew up, and Mom's divorce had been final for less than a year. They found companionship in each other, and that was enough for a time. They were stationed apart for a year shortly after they were married. Mom was sent to Hawaii and Dad went back to England.

There's a picture of them on a bed, dating or newlyweds, lying on a plush mink blanket. Dad's hand is lost in her messy brown perm, and they're kissing in a way I've never seen them kiss, in a way I'm not sure they've ever kissed each other since. Two people I have never met. In Hawaii, my mother quit drinking and found Jesus; she quit swearing and the Spirit moved her to speak in tongues. She ran nighttime miles around the lighted flight line to clear her head. My father reconnected with his ex-fiancé and sent my mother a letter he asked her to tear up without opening after a change of heart, which of course she didn't do. I understand I am my mother's daughter. Self-destructive, curious to a fault, distrusting, and fiercely protective of herself—her heart is a guarded thing and my father will never know it wholly. Over twenty-five years together and still there are still folds of her heart too precious to let him see. Corners so dark I wonder if her god can even know them.

She wanted to leave him early on, but the Bible says if the man wants you to stay, you should stay, and he wasn't ready to let her go. My father would rather be unhappy than alone. She didn't re-enlist and moved to England to be with him. He had no interest in changing, no interest in her newfound religion, and so they existed together. *Roommates*, she's said. With the way she talks about that time, I'm not quite sure how it happened, but she found out she was pregnant with me. Me, the glue—*After I found out, that was it. I could never take you away from your father*—the chain that bound her to this life, to him.

Mom says they are happy now, together, and I can see that they are. *I love your dad, and I know he loves me. We're good together,* she says. They have their routines and they look out for each other. Mom still hates to cook, but does it anyway because Dad won't make anything that can't be toasted or microwaved. He buys her flowers once a week and leaves her colorful notes on a whiteboard on the side of the fridge every morning before he goes to the gym. This version of them took me a while to get used to because for most of my childhood I could not understand why they didn't just get a divorce. My mother's bitterness toward my dad was palpable, verbalized to me in moments of desperation and weakness from a young age, and if I was to believe the right person for me was out there somewhere, someone who would make me happy and make me better, then it followed that those people were out there for my parents too. Sometimes my heart still hurts for them because how could they have known how bad it would get before it got better? And then that hurt turns to fear. How can anyone ever know?

***

Skimming the shore for sea glass one gray, November morning, Mom and I found a pair of seagulls caught on two hooks of the same iridescent lure. She sent me back to the house for pliers and when I returned she had me slick one of the bird's wings down tight against its body to hold as she worked the hook from its beak. It thrashed against us, but Mom was able to loose the hook and the bird was left with nothing more than

16

a hole, a little scar for remembering. I released its feathery body onto the sand and it took flight. We continued to work on the second gull, but it didn't fight us like the other one had and was losing a lot of blood. After fifteen minutes of twisting and prying, Mom took up the bird in her slender hands and tossed it onto the rocks, her gold wedding band catching the sunlight over the bay, the gull in total surrender, plastic fish dangling from its mouth.

GENTLE CARE VETERINARY CLINIC
PET EUTHANASIA CONSENT FORM

Date: 03/03/2016

Owner's Name: Brenna Womer; though, I can't help but feel she's Neil's too, still. Maybe it's because he chipped in half the money to have her spayed. Maybe it's the memory of him washing her in a Rubbermaid bin on our back porch, wearing the threadbare button-up I bought him at a thrift store, his bare feet stuck with bits of dead grass. It's been over two years since I left, since he and I have spoken, but we got Danza together, and, if it were me, I would want to know.

Patient's Name: Danza (Tiny Danza, Danza Brown, Danny, Danny Doo, Danzalina, Bean, Beany, Danza Bean, Punk, Punky Brewster, Punky Rooster, Baby Girl)

Owner's Address: In a loft that's too big for just me since the last guy moved out — he and I were never going to work. We ran out of things to talk about on our second date and spent a year in silence, playing on our phones. He was allergic to dogs, so my parents took Danza; now sometimes Dad calls me by her name. When Neil and I got her she was so small, five-pounds tiny. We had a house and a life and a love that worked, a love that felt like love. Not all of it does, you know? Some of it feels like loyalty or guilt or laziness; sometimes it only feels like reciprocation. He and I drove to Birch Tree, Missouri and met a woman from Pet Finder in front of a gas station built to look like a log cabin just off the highway, two hours from home. Our home.

Microchip number: I never did have hers activated, though I would absent-mindedly push at the pill-shaped lump just under her pink skin and short hair, little body covered in eyelashes, during movie nights on the green, tweed couch we found at the Salvation Army.

Age: Three, barely. We had been together for a year and a half when we got her, just eight weeks old — a companion for Neil's scruffy rat terrier, Wedge. We only lasted another year, because you know when you're 21 and, even when things are good, you assume there's better buried somewhere you haven't looked?

Species/Breed: The woman handed me this barrel-chested curl, warm but shaking from the rain and January cold. A dachshund she'd found in a trashcan and named Treasure, because one man's trash.	Sex: Sweet baby girl, pees with her crotch to the dirt. She never knew her sex, stitches in her overripe peach of a belly.
Weight: I don't know anymore, I guess Mom and Dad have a tendency to overfeed. There's a layer of fat now over her long ribcage, rolls at her neck, and her stomach is a soft, sagging paunch.	Color: Brown everything, just like me.

Would you like a necropsy (autopsy) to determine COD? I know the cause — another slipped disc. Shit started slipping, and she went numb. The medication's run out but didn't seem to do much for the pain any way. There is no cure and even if she gets better this time the chances are it'll happen again, so this is it. She can't keep living like this

I ask my animal's remains be cared for in the following way: You gave me a paper with my options — return of body for home burial, cremation and return of ashes, cremation and disposal of ashes, or, simply, disposal — and I don't know which to choose because I'm running out of Neil. The paper-thin pint glass we brought back from Kansas City cracked in the dishwasher, right through the little crown etched below the lip. The rose in the drained bottle of Irony Cabernet from our last Valentine's together snapped in half on the window sill when I drew the blinds. The house his sister sold, where we danced to "Call Me Al," drunk, in the kitchen after the Super Bowl, the one where his brother-in-law proposed at half-time and we all cried as Bruno Mars danced across the screen in a gold suit jacket, Panza hiding in the lining of the couch for all the excitement. I don't have much left of him that I can hold onto, but ashes might be worse than nothing. And there isn't any home to take her back to. Not any more.

Brenna E. Worre
(Signature)

Paperweight

Weed smoked gone from rolling paper
down to roach paperclip.
He paperbound her wrists,
pushed inside, paper-sack deep.

Months and no wallpaper peeled and shed,
no toilet paper red, so she went
to the clinic.
Lobby waits with *Marie Claire*,
The View on mute;
not-today's newspaper print.
She should've come sooner.
Leaned back on a fresh stretch of tissue paper,
a mobile overhead like a crib—
paper crane, paper tiger, paper plane.

The doctor asked *okay*, then paper cut.
Paperweight on paper plate;
she held the nurse's hand.
In the recovery room, no vinegar
or brown paper bag, but a cookie
for the sugar in her glass-paper blood.
A friend drove her home to thick pads
papered over Hanes Her Way.

IUD

It was Halloweentime, and so the nurse had clipped a phosphorescent bug to her scrub-top pocket. It hung heavy over the tray of tools she was holding for the gynecologist, and I watched it slowly slip, unclip, and land beside the copper T. When the doctor had measured the inside of me, he said he thought my sacred space was too small, unaccommodating, though I did meet the minimum requirement set by the manufacturer.

Would you like to proceed, he asked.

The beetle was there on the tray—

Go on, I said.

—next to molded copper.

The doctor took up his pincers, curved and studded to grip like Dungeness cracked at my annual birthday lunch. (Twenty-four and wearing a bib that said, *ITS MY BIRTHDAY AND ALL I GOT WAS CRABS.*)

The nurse didn't notice the doctor grab the bug from the tray; the doctor didn't notice the beetle in his claw as he reached into the dark, its transition from milky green to neon—a childish magic I believed in till the day I learned. He leaned up from between my legs, smacked the glove from his right hand, and said, *Success!* But for days after I could feel it moving, pipe-cleaner antennae feeling for the thresholds of fallopian tubes, and, finding their way, bottlebrush pain as they pushed into the wet and soft of me. The elytra worked to open, and I could feel their pressure at my walls; tarsi scraped and mandible clipped at endometrium. I went in for an emergency checkup, told them something wasn't right.

The pain, I said, sweat-soaked, and the same nurse took me in for an ultrasound, with nothing attached, now, to her scrub top pocket.

She wobbled the wand through cold gel at my lower abdomen and stopped over the implant. Soothed by megahertz, the thing lay still and haloed, phosphorescence in black and white, but no movement, and no pain.

Looks fine to me, hon, the nurse said. *Everything's right where it should be. How's your pain?*

Better, I said, but all I could see was the glow of sawtooth feelers and tips of creeping paper wings.

Motherlode

I want to be a mother but only on Sundays, yelling at them not to dirty their best in the woods behind the church. French Roast Folgers, Styrofoam cups, single serving Coffee-mate creamers, and Sweet'N Low packets that cause cancer like microwaves and cellphones, but we use them anyway because God is in control. I layer Oreo crumbs, Jell-O pudding, and Cool Whip in hand-me-down Pyrex for the potluck after second service. Don't doodle in the hymnal; shirttail tucked; eyes closed when we pray; take the grape juice from the inner circle—the wine is for Mommy; don't eat the bread, *the body*, before Pastor blesses it.

I want to be a mother when she has ballet at the little studio downtown; when his number is painted on my cheek for Friday night football; during the hour we spend making brownies and then licking the bowl, and in the thirty seconds it takes them to tear through their Christmas Eve stockings.

I want to be a mother, but only during the in-between times when I'm not fucking it up. When I'm not giving them a reason to hate me, hate the world, hate themselves. Early on, when they're fresh things, in those quiet night hours as they feed from my body, looking at me or past me— my connection to the realm of spirits, to God the Father, the Mother. My portal to a higher, better place before they learn to be here, to be human.

I want to be a mother before my daughter learns what she is to the world, before she gets angry at me for telling her the way things are, for breaking that beautiful spell as my own mother did. Before she spreads her legs for the first, the could-be, the why-won't-you, the true, the broken, and the anything-to-fill-this-hole kinds of love. We are not princesses.

I want to be a mother before I hate my son for what's between his legs: the soft, pillowy flesh he'll learn to wield like a sword. Let me be a mother before he realizes the power he has. Before boys will be boys and all guys do it and that's just the way men are. When he's brand new and sliding out of me, when he's latched on and drinking, when he bathes with his sister and kisses her on the mouth—before the world teaches them their place.

I want to be a mother, because I'm supposed to want to be a mother. But as I sat waiting for the nurse to come back with pregnancy-test results, a picture of two kids in a cornfield taped to her name badge, it wasn't a choice. It wasn't want. It was a thing that was happening, like an earthquake or daylight saving time. And even if I decided to say *No, no thank you* or *Not now, not yet*—even if I slept through the quake and refused to set my clocks back—still, forever, once, I was a mother. I was the one who would love and ruin them, the one they'd respect and blame. I was the one who'd know their bodies first, their minds, before they knew themselves, and keep their secrets before they understood there were any to keep. With a cocktail of fear and want, no and yes, me and all their potential in my belly, I was—for however brief a time—Mother.

All-Containered

Smoke apart the closed
and fire the remains;
add pears, something
green, to the kitchen.

Own up to the life locked
in the washroom; white,
but for soot-black froth
from lip to gummy lip,
and blue feet.

Use a word that crunches
like a sun-bleached egg
in the mouth and throat
because you didn't ask
for a *miracle* but got one
anyway, would prefer a life
of quiet good and discomfort
to these grand gestures
and tragic oversights
of the Universe.

Understand you can be
nothing or everything to
this world, that there is
no in-between, and that
to be nothing is not to
have or do nothing, but
to live and die in wet
cement. And to be every-
thing is not to have and
do everything, but to
watch all the nothing
in slow-motion from
the grass.

Hypochondria, or The Disease

arrhythmia, *n.*
Want of **rhythm** or regularity; *spec.* of the pulse.
[Two fingers at wrist or neck: *I am, I am, I am.* Before **diagnoses;** the old bray
of my **heart** to remind me, still, I exist.   [**anxiety; panic**
[skips beats, but only before **orgasm;** only   **disorder; depression.**
while kneading dough.   [Lexapro; Klonopin;
[*"*We'd have to   Paxil; Ambien.
get your boy-
friend in here
to test out that theory," the doctor said.
A joke—I laughed. Thought, *No, we*
really wouldn't.

bacterial vaginosis, *n.*
Bacterial overgrowth in the **vagina.**
[Prescribed: clindamycin. [**he** doesn't examine before diagnosis.
[the old man in blue jeans, no lab coat; shadowed by a young man,
nervous, with a **clipboard.**
[shuffles papers while the doctor takes a
phone call on his cell.
[It's an automated survey.

[is right.

["You don't have *fucking* carpal tunnel," **he** says, letting our breakfast burn in the pan.
carpal tunnel syndrome, *n.*
Median nerve compression in the wrist's carpal tunnel, characterized by a burning or
tingling pain in the hand, sometimes with **sensory loss** and muscle weakness, associated
with work that involves **repetitive movements.**   [for **days** I can't feel my hands.
                                    [A part-time job frosting   [after the first **attack.**
                                      cupcakes; the signature swirl.   ["Panic," the
                                                                                     doctor says. "A
                                                                                     disorder."

early-onset Alzheimer's disease, *n.*
A type of **dementia** that causes problems with memory, thinking, and behavior. Symptoms
usually   [Nanny **Betty,** my father's mother, who doesn't know who I am anymore.
develop slowly   [my middle name, Elizabeth, for **her.**
and worsen over time   [blood is mine.
becoming severe enough to interfere with **daily tasks.**
                                      [bringing a cup to my mouth without spilling.
                                      [punching in the code for our apartment door.
                                      [remembering the word for *pen.*
                                      [buttoning my shirt.

[Rarely, a person may develop GBS in the days or weeks after receiving the **flu shot.**

[left arm.

Guillain–Barré syndrome, *n.*

An acute form of peripheral nerve damage often preceded by a respiratory infection and the most common cause of ascending **paralysis.**

[No sleep, and I can't feel my feet—numb and soft and dead as dough, but I know not to wake him for this. He doesn't like the **new me.**

[scared

[**weak**

["You should be stronger than this."

[**crazy**

["It's like you're a different person."

["I can't do life like this."

[I Learned the Hard Way

[No One Told Me

[list: **Things** My Mother Should've Told Me

[garbage

[rebound

human papillomavirus, *n.*

(or HPV) A group of over **150 viruses, each** assigned its own **number**,

that can lead to cancers of the mouth,   [that condoms **don't protect** against.   [strain   [**High-risk**: 16 & 18

throat, anus, rectum, penis, **cervix**, *vagina*,   [31, 33, 45, 52, & 58.

and vulva, though most   [**cervical cancer**

cases of HPV **disappear**   [the leading cause.

on their own.   [like my mother's

when she was 19.

[**like mine** at 23.

[but **not before** five pap smears in two years.   [LEEP: Loop Electrosurgical

[**colposcopy** for biopsy; talk of **cauterization**.   Excision Procedure

[risks: bleeding

Greek →

→ infection

infertility

"to look at a hollow womb."

hypochondriasis, *n.*

Chiefly characterized by the patient's unfounded belief that she is suffering from some serious bodily disease; characterized by a morbid preoccupation with one's bodily health together with unfounded beliefs and exaggerated anxieties of **real** or imagined ailments, usually the symptom of a neurotic disorder.

[**always**

[to me.

mad cow, *n.*

(or bovine spongiform encephalopathy) A fatal disease in cattle that causes degeneration of the brain and spinal cord. When transferred to humans, it is called variant Creutzfeldt-Jakob disease, and the **United Kingdom** was the country most affected by the **epidemic**, from 1986–1998.

[2001: FDA restricts blood donations from any people residing longer than three months in the UK **after 1980.**

[1992: Bury St. Edmunds, birthplace.
[1996–2000: RAF Mildenhall, resident.

[They will not take my blood for, what might lie in wait, **dormant**.

[Incubation period: unknown.

"It's *very* unlikely," the doctor says.

[me
[with **someone** who has **HPV**.
[**sex**
oral cancer, *n*
A **cancer** that develops in any part of the **mouth.**
["What about **Michael Douglas?**" I ask.
[the doctor says, "is full of shit."

[mine, after he's been inside me.
[his, between my legs.

[you never discussed.
["**deal-breaker**"
["What if I **don't want** one?"
[*n*. urgent entreaty or
solicitation.
[*n*. the act of trying to obtain something from someone.

pregnancy, *n*.
The **condition** of a **female** of being pregnant or with **child**; a(n) **instance** of this.
[assumed
Latin → **femina**
[a **woman**
Old English
wīf][mon
→ **wife** man
[inherent

before birth
←
prae][gnasci
Latin
←

sudden infant death syndrome, *n.*

[SADS

[adult

(or SIDS) The unexplained **death,** usually during **sleep,** of a seemingly healthy baby less than a year old.

[no **sleep,**

[but I try for it, on my back, the week I learn.

[They don't wake up when they stop **breathing**.

[It's harder for the lungs to fill and lift the body when lying face-down.

trauma, *n.* [*adj.* relating to the soul or mind.

A **psychic** injury, esp. caused by emotional shock, the **memory** of which is **repressed** and **remains** unhealed. [

[Lipton iced tea powder mix

[late afternoon through living room **curtains**

[closed

[a babysitter **without** a face

[a body

[carpet and wood

Latin

re–] → [manere →

again & again, to stay

Forever Blonde

We were together for a summer, the first one he'd ever spent away from his two little girls who were downstate with their mother. He called her *my ex* on our first couple of dates and then *Sally* for a handful after that, but it wasn't long before she was back to being *Sal*—a name I thought too endearing for someone he was trying not to love anymore.

On Saturdays we'd stay in pajamas and play cribbage at the dining room table. He'd make mug after mug of pour-over coffee, and at some point I'd go to the guest bathroom to take a shit, nothing to look at but family photos. I learned that Sally had homebirths and breastfed and that there was no chance he'd ever look at either of their beautiful girls without thinking of her.

Each new thing he learned about me seemed to fall into one of two categories—Like Sally or Unlike Sally—and soon he was trying to fix me with the bits of her he had left: old snowshoes so I wouldn't have to buy a pair that winter, too-small tampons under the master bathroom sink, clonazepam in the medicine cabinet in case I forgot to pack my own, and a scalding bath for a UTI because she used to be a nurse and swore by it.

Sal will always be the mother of my children, he'd said, unprompted, more than once, but it got old, feeling him go limp in my mouth when her ringtone played; washing my dark brown hair with the dregs of her Forever Blonde shampoo.

Twenty-Something

I put on liquid eyeliner, but my dog
has cysts between her toes.

I drive to a bar and sit out front
with the engine running, then drive back home.

It's true, I call my mother, drunk, to ask about

                              her god, but the next day

I don't remember my questions, or her answers;
I can't recall the shape of the moon.

A student says he thinks I assign homework
so I'll have something to do when I go home.

It's true, I don't have anyone to listen to all

                              the nothing

 I have to say.

Sate

IV

On my fourth birthday the woman in line behind us at the bakery smelled like sex. It was mid-morning, and half-baked loaves were browning behind glass oven doors. The shop was warm to assist the yeast and gluten, dough rising beneath damp kitchen towels. Before the woman who smelled like sex arrived, the air was light and thick with loose flour and brewed coffee, cinnamon and fresh bread. When she walked in, the scent of the room took a sharp turn for warm water and salt, cumin and bergamot, not so sour as a lemon, but bitter like rind and rust. I didn't know the smell for what it was at the time—sweaty passion dried to olive skin at nape and spine and lower back, the pits of knees; tart, pheromone spice under arms and between thighs. If there had been a plant in the room it would have wilted. I wondered if the dough would still be able to rise with such an atmospheric shift, and, if it did rise, whether the bread it made might taste like her too.

My mother pulled me close to her side and handed me a tissue.

Cover your nose and mouth with this, she said, *like a mask*, and proceeded to cover her own just the same. But I liked the smell and lifted a corner of the tissue to breathe it in.

The baker acknowledged the woman and then asked how old I was as she poured whole milk into a bowl of powdered sugar. Whisking the extra glaze for my birthday cinnamon roll, she watched as my mother bent my right thumb into my right palm and held up my hand by the wrist. My mother lifted the bottom of her tissue so we could see her mouthing the word *four*, and I could feel the arch of her over-plucked brows as she anticipated my own recitation of the number for the baker. But I was watching the woman in line behind us.

Her dress was pale yellow, thin cotton, and wrinkled from a handful of hours on the floor. She carried her sandals and a book under one arm; there was a little tattoo—of what, I can't recall—at the ankle of one of her bare feet. She winked when she saw me staring, to which I snapped my head down and noted, as my mother made plug-nosed chitchat with the baker, my own shoes on the wrong feet, the tips curving away from each other like a fork in the road.

When I looked back up at the woman, indulging curiosity, she was still looking at me. We had the same pageboy haircut, and so she said, as she mussed up her own with a free hand, *I like your hair*.

I smiled under my tissue.

We watched, the three of us in line, as the baker drizzled thick frost from the cage of the whisk over a single roll—my special, once-a-year, birthday breakfast.

Can you dress one more of those, please, while you're at it? asked the woman who smelled like sex.

My mother curled the lip of the white paper sack and handed it to me, not to be eaten until we got home to plate and fork and damp napkin, a plastic baggy for the leftovers she'd make certain I'd have, telling me when I was full instead of letting me feel the ache and stretch and sick of it for myself.

As my mother poured cream into her coffee, everything taking her a bit longer than usual with just one free hand, the woman who smelled like sex ate her cinnamon roll from a square of parchment paper at a table for two, her feet up and resting on the opposite chair. She took bites so big she couldn't chew them with her mouth closed and ate without regard for the frosting at her upper lip. The sealed curl of the paper bag that held my own roll was turning damp, the fibers weakening in my overwrought clench.

Before my mother had finished saying goodbye to the baker, the woman who smelled like sex—on what appeared to be, for her, a most ordinary morning—having disappeared an iteration of my very special, once-a-year, birthday breakfast, brushed crusted sugar from tabletop to floor and left the shop, with no particular sense of urgency.

VII

I couldn't sleep, so I left the guest bed my mother and I were sharing and turned on *Full House* in my grandparents' living room. My grandfather had already switched off the lighted magnifying glass over his stamp collection and had retired from his desk for the night. With my thighs stuck to their brown leather couch, my great-grandmother's hideous scrap afghan over my lap, it was then I had an itch where I'd never had an itch before, an itch that, in the scratching, led to a new sensation altogether. Scratching turned to rubbing, which settled into a comfortable rhythm that seemed, some-how, deeply familiar—muscle memory without the memory itself. With the Tanners watching from the television nightlight, my hand moved in a way it had been waiting to move, fingering keys and hammering strings, the pumping of feet on the pedalboard. I could hear the music of a pipe organ, just one rank at first, quietly, and then another—a familiar Sunday school song:

It was on a Monday somebody touched me; it was on a Monday some-body touched me; it was on a Monday somebody touched me; it must've been the hand of The Lord.

The music played on, building, through Tuesday and Wednesday and Thursday. In church we were supposed to stand on the day we were saved, but because I couldn't remember the day, the moment, I denied my flesh and became a creature of the Spirit, I stood on Sunday. The organ beat on in a weekend crescendo, and my toes pointed the way I'd learned in the ballet class I'd quit after two weeks; I reared my chin into my neck and arched my back, and it was then I saw my mother in the doorway.

XI

The Altus Air Force Base Community Activities Committee got the idea to stock a decommissioned swimming pool with lake water and trout for kids to catch, so many fish you couldn't drop a line in without catching one. Looking down at the water, you could see them flopping over each other, too many bodies, too many walls. I went with my father. He hated fish but liked taking me to these sorts of events—a thing done together so we could say it was done.

I'd had my first period the month before, a sudden damp between my legs while my mother and I browsed at the Christian bookstore. I'm sure she had told my father, but he hadn't said anything about it to me. And now we were fishing. The limit was three, which I caught in three casts, deriving little satisfaction from the lack of effort, of mystery. We took my fish to the cleaning station where men from my father's squadron waited with fillet knives at a table next to the defunct lifeguard stand. One of them slid his hooknosed knife the length of the first fish's stomach, and at once I felt the dull hook-and-snag of a seam ripper deep inside my own, a spasmodic roiling as the man reached inside to loose a mess of slick string and organs with a bloodied glove.

This one was a lady, the man said, scraping peach roe from its swollen gut. *You want the eggs, Chief,* he asked my father, who made a face that answered no.

With that, the man slid his knife-edge along the table and pushed the eggs into the trash bin at the end. I could feel the hot red wet at my inner thigh and told my dad I had to pee.

IXX

I hadn't yet felt the raw slick of him inside of me. He said:

I just don't think we can experience the full spectrum *of intimacy with something synthetic between us. The barrier is kind of like a metaphor, don't you think?*

He took off his pants, always black-turned-brown at the thighs and back pockets from espresso he ground and tamped and poured part-time for me and the other hundred college students who wandered into the coffee shop each day. He was five years older, handsome, elusive, and graduated, an illustrator always sketching people uglier than they were in real life. Eventually he and I would move in together, and for two years he would insist we wash our clothes in separate loads of laundry.

It had been a week since I requested a prescription for the pill, a week since my doctor asked me to recall the Elmer's glue I'd used in grade school, how it might piece together one of the lives waiting to live or die inside of me.

Always use backup, he'd said. *This is no guarantee.*

The barista, in boxer briefs, pulled off his black-brown v-neck.

It's the difference between fucking and making love, he said, and I stared at his wide, pepperoni nipples.

I wanted to know if, when he came, I'd feel it inside like spray from a garden hose, like the chocolate gush from a molten lava cake. If maybe the glue might piece together more than someone else inside of me. And so we fucked for the first time without anything between us.

It was six pumps before, *I'm coming*—syllables flaking from his lips like soup crackers: *Baby, baby, baby.*
When he rolled off me his dick slapped wet against my thigh, and he put his hand on mine. Smiling, sweaty, he said, *You don't wanna wait long to clean up. It'll run right out of you.*

The only thing I hadn't expected was for it to feel like nothing at all.

XXX

I'll turn thirty at 12:07 PM, and they'll start to fall, all of them at once, eggs in a 7-Eleven bathroom. The first one will plop into the bowl, followed by another, and then two, out of me like raw, peeled shrimp. Two at a time, then three and four together, and soon the bowl will be full. I'll stand up, half-naked, with eggs falling to the tiled floor. In a panic, I'll scoop them from the toilet and fill the wastebasket, but they'll start falling half-a-dozen at a time and I won't be able to keep up. I'll cup them into the sink, mashing them to the sides with my fist, mortar and pestle, pressing them down the open drain, pulp between my fingers and under my nails. Hundreds, and then thousands, so I'll stop, ankle-deep, and let them fall. Globules the size of gumballs, clear and gelatinous, pink and blue veins running through, some with sprouts of hair and chips of teeth at their centers. When the line approaches my knees, they'll start to slow, like popping corn in the microwave. I'll wade through them for my purse atop the tank, squish my hands through the mess for the pants at my feet. When I heave the door open, they'll spill out into the aisles of corn chips and condoms and chocolate-covered peanuts, and a woman not much older than myself will lift her child from the ground, hold its face to her own in horror.

With eggs in my shoes, trapped in the crotch of my underwear, I'll walk for the register and try to remember whether I was the baker or the mother or the daughter or the woman who smelled like sex.

Acknowledgments

Pieces in this collection have appeared in the following magazines and journals:

"Empire Blue" in *New South*

"Paperweight" in *Public Pool*

"Pet Euthanasia Consent" in *The Pinch*

"Motherlode" in *Booth*

"All-Containered" in *Carve Magazine*

"Hypochondria, or The Disease" in *DIAGRAM*

"Forever Blonde" in *Hippocampus*

"Twenty-Something" in *DIALOGIST*

"Sate" in *The Normal School*

About the Author

Brenna Womer is an essayist, poet, and fiction writer living in Michigan's snowy Upper Peninsula. She received her BA and MA in English from Missouri State University and is an MFA candidate at Northern Michigan University, where she teaches and serves as an associate editor of *Passages North*. Her work has been published by *The Normal School, Indiana Review, DIAGRAM, The Pinch, New South*, and other magazines. Her essay "Wüsthof Silverpoint II 10-Piece Set" was named a Notable of the year in *The Best American Essays* 2017. This is her debut collection.

C&R PRESS CHAPBOOKS

C&R Press hosts two chapbook selection periods from June to September and November to March coupled with a reading in New York City each year. The Winter Soup Bowl and Summer Tide Pool Chapbook Series are open to new and established writers in poetry, fiction, essay and other creative writing.

2017 WINTER SOUP BOWL

Heredity and Other Inventions
by Sharona Muir

On Inaccuracy
by Joe Manning

2016 Summer Tide Pool

Cuntstruck
by Kate Northrop

Relief Map
by Erin M. Bertram

Love Undefined
by Jonathan Katz

2016 Winter Soup Bowl

Notes from the Negro Side of the Moon
by Earl Braggs

A Hunger Called Music: A Verse History in Black Music
by Meredith Nnoka

OTHER C&R PRESS TITLES

NONFICTION

Women in the Literary Landscape by Doris Weatherford, et al

FICTION

Made by Mary by Laura Catherine Brown
Ivy vs. Dogg by Brian Leung
While You Were Gone by Sybil Baker
Cloud Diary by Steve Mitchell
Spectrum by Martin Ott
That Man in Our Lives by Xu Xi

SHORT FICTION

Notes From the Mother Tongue by An Tran
The Protester Has Been Released by Janet Sarbanes

ESSAY AND CREATIVE NONFICTION

Immigration Essays by Sybil Baker
Je suis l'autre: Essays and Interrogations by Kristina Marie Darling
Death of Art by Chris Campanioni

POETRY

Dark Horse by Kristina Marie Darling
Lessons in Camouflage by Martin Ott
All My Heroes are Broke by Ariel Francisco
Holdfast by Christian Anton Gerard
Ex Domestica by E.G. Cunningham
Like Lesser Gods by Bruce McEver
Notes from the Negro Side of the Moon by Earl Braggs
Imagine Not Drowning by Kelli Allen
Notes to the Beloved by Michelle Bitting
Free Boat: Collected Lies and Love Poems by John Reed
Les Fauves by Barbara Crooker
Tall as You are Tall Between Them by Annie Christain
The Couple Who Fell to Earth by Michelle Bitting

CPSIA information can be obtained
at www.ICGtesting.com
Printed in the USA
FFOW03n0628250218
45217250-45801FF

9 781936 196623